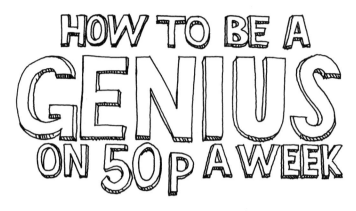

HOW TO BE A GENIUS ON 50P A WEEK

HOW TO BE A GENIUS ON 50P A WEEK

BY JASON COWAN (13½)

illustrations by TIM STONEMAN (12¾)

a Charles Herridge book
Sidgwick & Jackson

© Copyright Charles Herridge Ltd 1984

Published by Charles Herridge Ltd
Woodacott, Northam, Bideford
Devon EX39 1NB
Typeset by Lens Typesetting, Bideford
Printed by New Interlitho SpA, Milan

ISBN 0 283 99121 6

Distributed by Sidgwick & Jackson Ltd
Tavistock Chambers, Bloomsbury Way
London WC1A 2SG

CONTENTS

*Genius H.Q.,
The Kingdom of Fife,
SCOTLAND.*

Hi there, Stupid!

Yeah, that's right STUPID. Which is exactly what you are. At the moment anyway. The whole purpose of this book is to change you from what you are at the moment into what I am. That is to say, a genius. [Who is this bighead? – Ed.]

My name is Jason Cowan. I am tall, handsome, well-built, and have the natural advantage of being Scottish. The fact that other people seem to think I am big, hairy, spotty and daft is irrelevant. My achievements have been stupendous considering that I am forced to work on a weekly pocket money budget of a mere 50p a week.

So you want to be a genius like me, eh? Well, firstly you must realise that it's going to be no easy matter changing you from a small, skinny, spotty and completely unhairy weakling into a muscular, tall, good-looking, fur-covered genius. But I can do it. If you follow my instructions – to the letter – good looks, charisma, and a life of well-deserved luxury will be within your grasp. Yes! Fame! Fortune! Friends! All these and more can be yours on a mere 50p a week!

Unfortunately, as with all things, there is a good side and a bad side to being a genius. Confucius, he say "Where there is glamour, there is heartbreak". Confucius, he say too much for his own ruddy good. But sadly, this proverb bears true in all things it concerns, and geniosity is no exception. It takes years of insanity and the utmost dedication, a lonely vigil against the forces of normality. The path to genius is long and treacherous, and short cuts will only lead you into the bogs of ignorance. It is therefore necessary to obey all my instructions without hestitation. (For a start, you must send me lots of fan mail and large donations to the Jason Cowan Maintenance Fund.)

Before you start on this project, you must understand what a genius is. In order to give you a glimpse of the sort of overall outcome you should try to aim for, I attempted to interview a true genius. After a long and frenzied search, the only figure of ultimacy I could find was myself! So, pressganging a passing teenager, I "persuaded" him to start recording an interview with this "Ultimate Man" in the studios of Auchtermuchty Sound – a new radio station recently set up by a young entrepreneurial genius of my aquaintance who is not unlike me! (He is Me!) A transcript of this penetrating interrogation can be found on the opposite page.

And now, without further ado, you may begin your course. And remember – If anyone asks you if you have got this book, deny it at all costs! You don't want every Angus, Neil and Ian knowing the secrets of your success. [And you don't want the men in white coats coming to take you away – Ed.]

Yours sincerely,

Jason Cowan (aged 13 years 11 months)

6

TRANSCRIPT OF INTERVIEW WITH J. COWAN, GENIUS.
RECORDED AT THE STUDIOS OF "AUCHTERMUCHTY SOUND".
DATELINE: TUESDAY

Ultimate Man (Me):	O.K. You may proceed with any questions you feel like asking.
Innocent Victim:	What am I doing here? And who are you?
Genius:	You are meant to be asking relevant questions about me, Jason Cowan, the Ultimate Symbol of Masculinity. You will find the script on your left.
Victim:	Oh, right . . . O.K., when did you first recognise in yourself the signs of your potential brilliance?
Genius:	Ever since I built my first Nuclear Power Station out of Lego, I felt I was kind of . . . *better* than my friends.
Victim:	Does anyone else acknowledge your superiority?
Genius:	Alas, very few people are aware of the untapped brain power that is inside my handsome head.
Victim:	Ah, yes, that's another thing. Have you always been so irresistible to the opposite sex?
Genius:	Yes.
Victim:	Despite your dazzling superiority, many people find you rather . . . strange.
Genius:	Genius is always confused with madness. Besides, as I stress on many occasions, a genius is *not* the same as everyone else.
Victim:	I see. I hope that has silenced your critics.
Genius:	If it hasn't, my Private Army will!
Victim:	Ah, yes, your Private Army. Many people find them excessively violent . . .
Genius:	Say that again and I'll have you shot!
Victim:	Gulp! I see! What does Deborah Anderson think of you putting her name in print?
Genius:	She has not expressed any discontent.
Victim:	She's probably scared to because of the Private Army! Ha, Ha, Ha!

Background noise off

Genius:	Next please.
2nd Victim:	At last! Is it really you? THE Jason Cowan? Wow! I'm your greatest fan!
Genius:	Look, Deborah, I've told you time and time again not to come and see me whilst I'm working. Now, stop that, and put me down. Wait for me upstairs. Oh, and send in the next Vict. . . . I mean Interviewer.
3rd Victim:	mumble, mumble, mumble, mumble.
Genius:	You may get off your knees. Do you know where the script is?
Victim:	Er, Yes. Let's see . . . O.K., why do you enjoy playing Rugby?
Genius:	It's VIOLENT. And it's excellent training for the battlefield. All the members of the team are in my Private Army.
Victim:	Have any fatalities occurred in your Private Army?
Genius:	I'm sorry, my army is in many ways like the SAS. I cannot answer that question. No comment. And please do not ask about my army again.
Victim:	Well! I don't see why I can't . . .

Genius:	Believe me folks, there are some things you are better off not knowing.

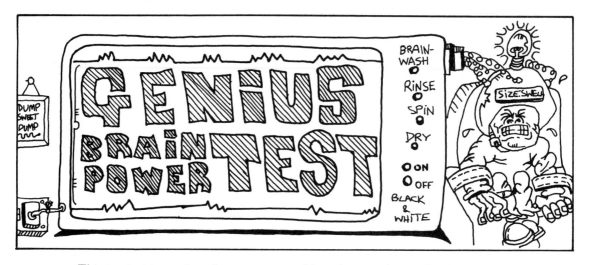

This is a test to see how brainy you are. Now that you know the diverse and complicated reasons behind it you may proceed with the examination. If, as is very likely, you get all the answers wrong, read the rest of this book. You will then be a genius and will find that you can complete it with no trouble at all.

SCOTTISH WORDSEARCH

How many Scottish words can you find in this map of Scotland?

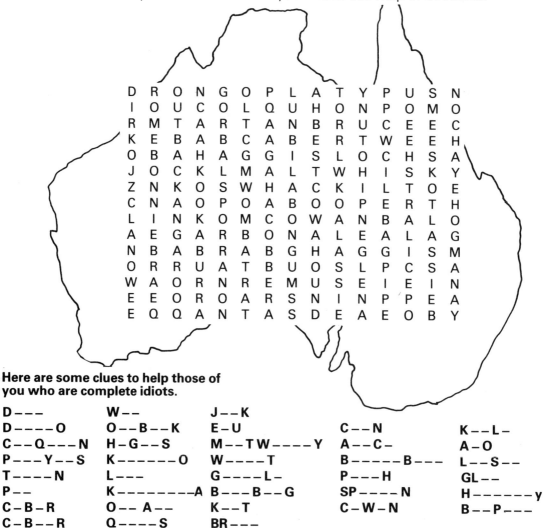

Here are some clues to help those of you who are complete idiots.

D – – –	W – –	J – – K		
D – – – – O	O – – B – – K	E – U	C – – N	K – – L –
C – – Q – – – N	H – G – – S	M – – T W – – – – Y	A – – C –	A – O
P – – – Y – – S	K – – – – – – O	W – – – – T	B – – – – – B – – –	L – – S – –
T – – – – N	L – – –	G – – – – L –	P – – – H	GL – –
P – –	K – – – – – – – – A	B – – – B – – G	SP – – – – N	H – – – – – – y
C – B – R	O – – A – –	K – – T	C – W – N	B – – P – – –
C – B – – R	Q – – – – S	BR – – –		

Answers: *Dirk, Colquhoun, tartan, caber, wee, haggis, loch, och aye, Jock, malt whisky, gorbals, kilt, Bruce, clan, bonnie brae, Perth, sporran, Cowan, lassie, glen, Hogmanay, bagpipe. Drongo, platypus, pom, cobber, outback, kangaroo, kookaburra, qantus, emu, billabong, Alice, Koala, and abo aren't Scottish, you idiots.*

8

MAZE

Find your way to Deborah's bedroom without getting clobbered by her mum.

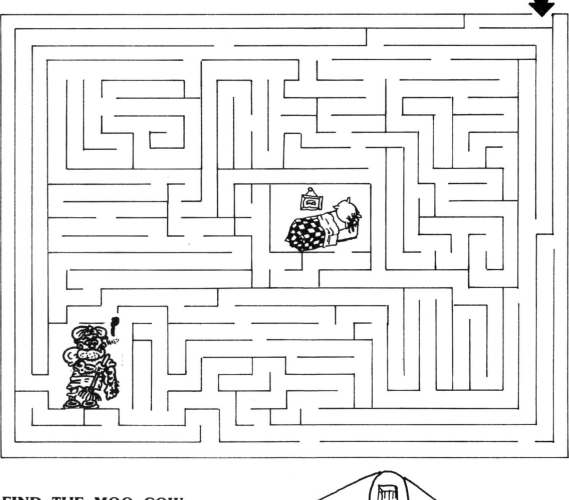

FIND THE MOO COW

How many Highland Cattle can you find in this picture?

Not surprisingly, the genius brain is an extremely complicated sort of chemical computer kind of thing. But what makes the genius brain better than ordinary, boring brains? Well, to explain this we have to go back to basics. And rather surprising basics they are too. The brain is, in fact, a massive home for hundreds of thousands of little grey "brain men".

Some of these brain men are lucky enough to have jobs in certain areas of the brain. The cleverest areas of the brain are the ones with the highest population of hard-working brain men. The stupidest parts of your brain are the parts with the highest population of idle, unemployed brain men. So now that you know what goes on in there, be kind to your brain in the future. Every time you head-bang, 1200 little grey men fall down dead!

Now let us look at the genius brain with its different sections.

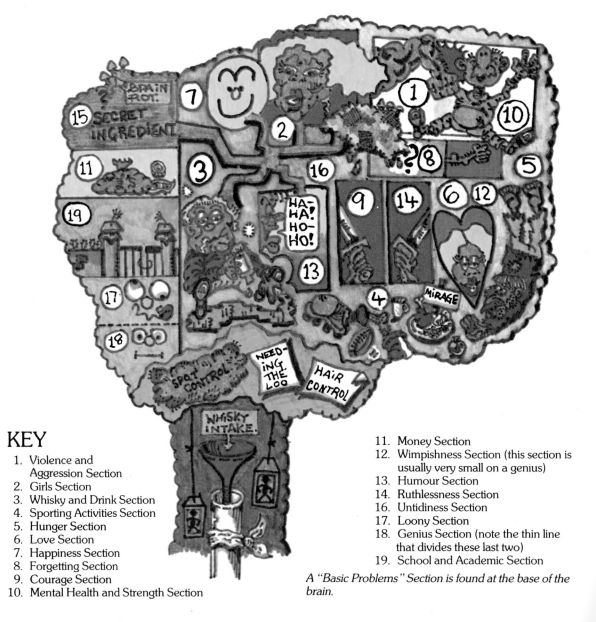

KEY

1. Violence and Aggression Section
2. Girls Section
3. Whisky and Drink Section
4. Sporting Activities Section
5. Hunger Section
6. Love Section
7. Happiness Section
8. Forgetting Section
9. Courage Section
10. Mental Health and Strength Section
11. Money Section
12. Wimpishness Section (this section is usually very small on a genius)
13. Humour Section
14. Ruthlessness Section
16. Untidiness Section
17. Loony Section
18. Genius Section (note the thin line that divides these last two)
19. School and Academic Section

A "Basic Problems" Section is found at the base of the brain.

HOW YOUR BRAIN SHAPES YOUR HEAD

As the different parts of your brain develop they need more and more brain men to keep them going. Obviously, the sections with the greatest number of workers require more space to keep all the brain men in. So they just stretch as more and more brain men are squashed inside. As the shape of the brain changes so does the shape of the head, so you can easily tell what sort of character a person has by simply looking at or feeling their head.

Here are some tell-tale signs:
A head that looks like an upside down Doc Marten Boot indicates an extremely violent personality. This is because of the growth of the violence section.

What to do: If you want to keep your aggression try headbanging. This will compress the protruding forehead and also leave you with such a thumping headache that you will be highly irritable.

Problem: every time you headbang 1200 brain men die.

This persons likes a wee dram . . .

And this person often needs the loo.

A head with a lump on the right hand side shows that the owner is both in love and a wimp – a particularly painful combination.

This poor chap is always hungry – perhaps he's got worms.

And this brilliant person is a genius! *[or he could be a loony. Ed.]*

11

All right. So I've got the odd pimple here and there. But that doesn't mean to say I can't have *rugged* good looks. Some of the greatest men in history have had the odd spot. For example . . . well, me. No, wait! I've got it. Oliver Cromwell had warts! And please God don't let me turn out like Rod Stewart.

Now, being a genius you would expect me to have an infallible cure for spots, and of course you're right. In fact I've got three infallible cures. I haven't had time to try them all out yet – but perhaps you would like to help me out with my research. Write and let me know how you get on.

MIRACLE CURE NO. 1

Suicide is a cure that is usually infallible. Take a long length of rope and make a loop using a round turn and two half hitches (a double granny will do if you're very stupid). Tie your rope to the branch of a tree, put your head through the loop and relax completely. The desired result will only be obtained if your whole body weight is taken by the rope. If you find that your feet are still in contact with the ground, tie the rope to a higher branch and repeat the process until death occurs.

Once you are dead, someone will probably make funeral arrangements. If they forget to do so you can give them a stiff reminder by permitting your insides to rot. The result will be a particularly offensive smell and you will be surprised how quickly you are buried. Now all you have to do is allow yourself to rot completely. This makes way for a spot-free face, a face-free head, and, in fact, a head-free body. The next step is reincarnation. You can now be transferred to a new and completely spot-free body.

MIRACLE CURE NO. 2

For those opposed to the idea of suicide, I have devised a very effective Nitric Acid Cure. First, take your acid and pour it into a lead-lined basin. Then, taking care to protect your hands with heavy-duty rubber gloves, wash your face and any other affected area with the solution. You may experience a slight degree of agony during this part of the operation which may cause you to scream, call out for help, or possibly even to die. But never mind, the best cures always hurt the most, and you can be sure of a spot-free face after just one application.

MIRACLE CURE NO. 3

(for the desperate)

In the unlikely event of either of the two previous cures failing to solve the problem, No. 3 can be used as a last resort. Please note however, that the AUTHOR ACCEPTS NO RESPONSIBILITY FOR ANY ADVERSE RESULTS ARISING FROM THE USE OF THIS CURE. Half fill a washbasin with warm water taking care not to allow any of the liquid to come into contact with your delicate skin. Using tongs or a similar appliance, pick up a piece of soap. Remember to keep your face turned away as you do this or you will be overcome by the sickly smell of the noxious substance. Place the soap in the water and agitate it vigorously until a frothy emulsion is formed. Now, apply the disgusting solution to your face.

Once you have recovered consciousness, take a look in the mirror. You will be surprised how little the spots have faded! But do remember that this is a long-term method of treatment and it will be some years before the cure is effected. Personally, I am too young to be able to vouchsafe the results but my mum assures me it will work eventually.

Thrill to this latest game from Auchtermuchty Video Enterprises ™

The author wishes to inform you that this game is absolutely disgusting and very spotty people might find it extremely distressing and upsetting. If you feel you would be adversely affected please skip the next two pages.

BEAT THE PULLULATING PUSTULES AT THEIR OWN GAME

with your powerful armoury of anti-spot devices.

YES!

Blatt those Blackheads!

Pulverize those Pimples!

Whack those Warts!

Crush those Carbuncles!

Can Carbolic Soap, Antiseptic Spot Cream, Pure Loch Water, and Nitric Acid beat these video nasties?

THE RULES

The evil King Carbuncle has decided to make YOU his next objective. Already his hordes of nasties have entrenched themselves on your face. These fetid fearsomes include: The Blackhead Brigade; The Pimple Patrol; The Bellicose Boils; and The Wily Wicked Warts.

All you have to do is to splatter your spots with a chosen weapon.
SOAP SUDS may beat the odd blackhead
CLEARASIL could exterminate a pimple
PURE LOCH NESS WATER can annoy a big spot but
NITRIC ACID will shift almost anything – but BEWARE if this hits a clear patch of skin, you end up with a hole in your face!

Will the spots be able to avoid the acid?
Will you end up with holes in your face?
Will your supplies run out?
Will King Carbuncle take over your body?

It's all up to you in this thrilling game of Zap the Zits!

Scoring

Score the following points for a direct hit:

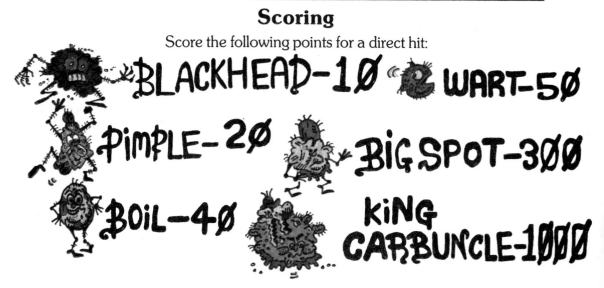

BLACKHEAD-10   WART-50

PIMPLE-20   BIG SPOT-300

BOIL-40   KING CARBUNCLE-1000

Hole in Face = minus 10 points.

MASSIVE MUSCLES IN A MONTH!

A beautiful face needs a beautiful body to go with it. You probably think that building a bronzed and muscular body means hours and hours in the gym doing horribly strenuous exercises and weeks and weeks of frying unpleasantly under a boring sunlamp. But you are wrong! These uninspired activities are much too strenuous, much too expensive, much too time-consuming, much too nasty and much too stupid for a budding genius like you.

So what do you do? As with so many things, Nature and El Guffo™ have the answer.

PORRIDGE INJECTIONS

Be very careful when injecting yourself with porridge. Make sure the porridge is cold. Hot porridge may give you an easier flow but it is not in the least beneficial. Also, take great care not to inject the stuff into your bloodstream. This is even less beneficial than using hot porridge. The porridge will fill out your body, but even though your arm, for example, is nice and bulky, you will still have to shape the porridge under your skin so that your arm looks muscle-shaped.

There are many ways of doing this. You could try tying strings round your limbs to compress the porridge, though you will undoubtedly have trouble in explaining them being there. Probably the only foolproof method is to buy yourself an El Guffo™ Armcompressor.

Porridge, however, is only a short term answer. Having the porridge go mouldy under your skin is highly unpleasant, and extracting old porridge and injecting new is a tedious weekly ritual. Exercise is really the only answer. But this doesn't mean hours of lifting huge weights or tugging futilely at Coworkers. A genius has better things to do with his valuable time.

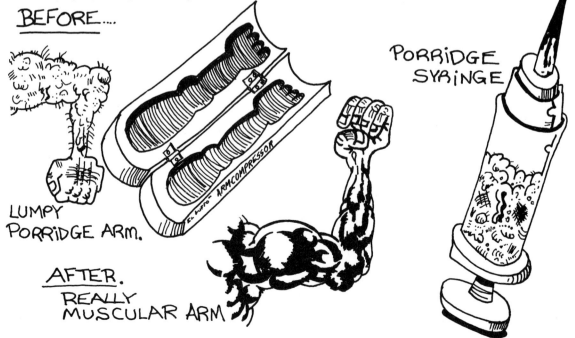

BEFORE....

LUMPY PORRIDGE ARM.

AFTER.
REALLY MUSCULAR ARM

PORRIDGE SYRINGE

Well, El Guffo™ has done it again, sinking to uncharted depths with this amazing

MUSCLE MACHINE

This developer can easily be adjusted to increase or decrease the amount of effort required to move. You can do this by adding or subtracting the weights and armour to increase or lighten your load, and by changing the number of elastic bands you have over your joints. This Supersuit should be worn underneath your clothes for constant effort throughout the day. If it gets a bit smelly, just take it off, give it a quick hose down, and put it back on as quickly as you can before your muscles start to get lazy and relaxed. Try to avoid swimming and other water sports when Suit Training. This can be both highly dangerous and embarrassing. It is, however, great fun wearing the suit when playing rugby and other violent sports as it offers extra strike power and also protection.

FROM PUKEY PINK TO BRAWNY BROWN

A pastey pink skin doesn't enhance your new beautiful body. *Real* men sport an even, dark tan. Sunbathing is boring and bad for you but my patent Brawny Bronzing Method is cheap, quick and infallible.

You will need:
    A bath
    Some water
    One gross (144) Teabags

Methods:

Day 1 1. Enter bathroom
        2. Turn on taps
        3. Place one dozen teabags in bath
        4. Take clothes off
        5. Get in bath and stay there

Day 2 Same as yesterday but use two dozen teabags.

Repeat each day until you have reached 144 teabags.

Special Note Don't forget to do behind your ears.

As with exercises you should get your tan gradually. People will notice if you suddenly turn from white to black overnight. To maintain your new bronzed body, a weekly tea bath will suffice.

ECONOMY TIP

This bronzing method will be very expensive if you have to start a fresh tea bath every day. A cheap tan can be obtained by adding 1 dozen tea bags to the original tea bath until 144 is reached. You may have to persuade the rest of your family to join you in your tannin(g) programme unless there is more than one bathroom in the house.

Even though exercises can help to develop what would otherwise be rather puny muscles, they can be bad for you if you don't eat the right kind of food. A bodybuilder's diet should contain plenty of roughage and nutritional fibre and very few calories. Lard and liquorice should also be avoided. All this sounds hideously complicated so I have devised a foolproof eating plan – Yes, it's the Revolutionary **G PLAN DIET!!!**

To avoid complications my diet specifies that you eat the same food *every* day. Once started on this diet, all my instructions should be adhered to or I cannot take responsibility for the outcome. In fact, El Guffo ™ can accept no responsibility for any fatalities which may occur as a result of this diet.

So here we go and Bon Appetit!

BREAKFAST:

1 plate of salty porridge; Haggis Pudding; milk laced with Whisky.

LUNCH:

Haggis served in the traditional manner with neaps (turnips to you Sassenachs), mashed potato and chips. Tot of Whisky to follow.

TEA or SUPPER:

Haggis slices served on oatcakes. Hot chocolate laced with Whisky.

That'll put hairs on your chest, eh, lad? As well as giving you severe constipation and making you permanently drunk. Well, we did say it was revolutionary. With this diet you can throw away all your bran and Ryvita. The Haggis is here to stay. Here is a diagram showing all the best cuts.

Key

1. Wing. Very tough. Tastes like beef.
2. Arm. Very unusual. Tastes like lamb.
3. Legs. Very stringy. Impossible to get on a fork. Few people know what haggis legs taste like.
4. Rear Leg (and Foot). Not much meat due to the extremely large and knobbly knee. What there is tastes like pork.
5. The main part of the Haggis, the part we usually eat. It's all pretty weird in here. Tastes like Haggis if you ask me.
6. The eyes. Are you kidding?

Many of you may think that all this eating the right foods and doing the right exercises is a waste of time. After all, what's the point? Be stilled, ye blasphemous tongues. Not only are bulging muscles considered immensely attractive, they can help you to build a promising career in the films. Well-built men are constantly in demand for barbarian movies. And you'll find it surprising how few people push you around . . .

A WORD ABOUT GRUNTIES

Oh, all right, I've left something out. Grunties. Yes, that's right, grunties. Grunties are three things that you find in your armpit. Well, they may not be there at the moment. They don't emerge from under the skin unless they are developed. All you have to do is this exercise.

And that is *all* you must do. You should not tamper with your armpit. Grunties find it hard to survive when they are continually being sprayed and rolled on.

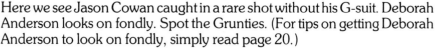

Here we see Jason Cowan caught in a rare shot without his G-suit. Deborah Anderson looks on fondly. Spot the Grunties. (For tips on getting Deborah Anderson to look on fondly, simply read page 20.)

A GENIUS'S GUIDE TO WOMEN

Let's face it lads, women are pretty essential to life as we know it. After all, who else is going to do the washing up, wash your smelly socks, tidy your bedroom? Occasionally they can also be of sentimental value.

In this field of human relationships, however, there can be problems. Take girlfriends. Or rather the lack of them. Traditional confessions to the girls usually result in "uggh!" "Get lost!" and other such pleasantries. If this sort of thing happens to you, then you're obviously doing something wrong. You've already got your muscles and your grunties sorted out, so what else are they after? I consulted Deborah Anderson on this matter and the three thing that attracted her most (to me) are:

1. My facial and bodily hair
2. My charming and witty personality and/or my ruthlessness
3. The way I tease and play hard to get.

Apparently women find hair very attractive. Hairy legs and armpits are not only cuddly but for many females symbolise manliness. Many of you may find problems growing all that hair. This could be because you're too young (the earliest you start to get hairy is about 12) or you may be too old (this refers to the bald patches you get when you're about my dad's age). If you're as old as my dad, then you've had it. If you're under 12 you can ask the doctor for hormone tablets but he'll probably tell you to wait a while.

Now let's work on your charming yet ruthless character. On the outside you must appear to be uncaring. No helping old ladies across the street. No doing errands for teachers. If anyone asks you to do anything like this simply say "No". The masses of girls you attract will be well worth the trouble. There is one small problem when you start to create this new image. If you fancy someone, how do you let them know that you are really quite charming? Simple. Let a rumour circulate that you are somewhat fond of the target in question, and that underneath that hard exterior you are incredibly loving and lovable. Her curiosity will be aroused and she will approach you to find out if what everyone says is true. Then, and only then, do you display the nice side of your nature. Immediately, your beloved is attracted to you, due to the subtle balance of these extremes of character.

But you must still tease her. If she says "Are you doing anything tonight?", then reply "Yes, I'm washing my hair". If she says "Would you like to go to the cinema?", then say "I think I've got a headache coming on". And if she says "Would you like to go for a filthy camping weekend?" then shout "YES PLEASE!!!"

Now that you've got your woman, what do you do with her? This is a very serious problem, because if you let her mooch around doing nothing she will soon start to get restless. When she has finished the washing up and dusting, encourage her to take up an absorbing hobby such as knitting you a new jumper or redecorating your bedroom. All this may sound a bit hard, but never mind, it's all part of your hard-man image, and she loves it.

Let's face it, some of us are not much good at attracting girls. Well, not so much some of *us* as some of *you*. I personally have no trouble. If you've done everything you've been told to do, and still not found anyone to darn your socks, there's one last resort.

El Guffo presents a unique opportunity

DATE-A-SCOT

The Date-a-Scot Service is a collection of very wonderful Scottish people, all desperate for money, and all personally vetted by me. Choose any Scot from the selection below at our special introductory offer price of 50p (plus £3.50 towards post and packing). Then, every month, we will send you another selection of superb Scots. If nothing strikes your fancy, simply tear up their pictures. All we ask is that you choose at least four Scots during your first year of membership of the Date-A-Scot Service.

HURRY HURRY HURRY Send your 50p (plus £3.50) now, before stocks run out, and become the proud owner of one of these wonderful Scottish people.

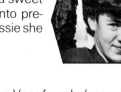

Sex: Female. **Personality:** Ah, such a sweet smile. That steel wool hair welded into presentable shape. What a bonnie wee lassie she is, as we say North of the Border.

Sex: Very female (according to Junkie). **Personality:** Junkie fancies her, but then he would.

Sex: All will soon be revealed. **Personality:** If you would like to make one of these, then simply take a mop and paper plate. Paint a funny face on the plate and stick it on the mop. (Courtesy of Blue Peter.)

Sex: Girl (believe it or not). **Personality:** Daft enough to join Date-A-Scot. 'Nuff said!

Sex: Not much of a surprise. **Personality:** Blue Peter thing to make Variation 113. You put this one in your garden and put peanuts up its nose to feed the birds.

Sex: Girl. **Personality:** A right swot. Also stupid enough to wear that excruciating Bell Baxter School uniform in possibly the most important photo of her life.

Sex:? **Personality:** Someone who gets very annoyed when people put question marks beside its sex.

Sex: Male. **Personality:** Did you know I've got to limit these captions to 36 words ? Well, I don't care, because the next one is just *so funny*. And besides the works of Cowan deserve longer than just . . .

[That's yer lot Cowan. You deserve to get lynched for this page. Ed.]

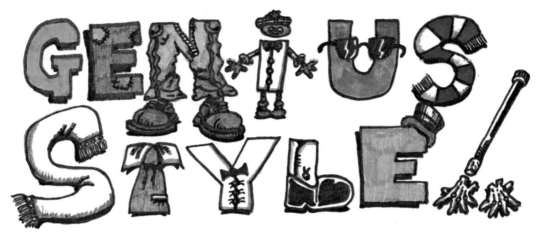

GENIUS STYLE!

A genius is a one off, a truly original, wonderful person. There are not many of us around. Most people are just clones. They wear uniforms in order to be like everyone else.

These forces of convention consist of:

Punks and Skinheads

Although they do not like to admit it, both Punks and Skinheads are clones of the same ilk. Both are extremely stupid and often do not know what they are doing as they seem to be permanently drunk or have tubes of glue stuck up their noses. They are very dangerous and are likely to kill me given half the chance [Publish and be damned – Ed.] Depite their horrific appearance Punks aren't quite as dangerous as Skinheads as they spend most of their time at the hairdressers or admiring the cut of their chains in front of the mirror.

Rating	Punks	Skinheads
Attraction	−10	−5
Style	−5	−10
Danger	+20	+50

Hippies

There are more of these around than you think and, although they look like decrepit wombles (Greenham rather than Wimbledon Common variety), they are

probably the "nicest" representatives of the forces of convention. Don't get too close to them though as you could get high on their breath. Could be worth cultivating – they may be heavily into peace (ugh!) but they usually come from upper class families and can get their hands on lots of money if approached in the right way (see Earn £10,000 a Year by Age 14).

Rating
Attraction	1
Style	5
Danger	−20

Wimps

Some very feeble persons are forced to wear uniforms by schools, parents, scoutmasters and other authoritarian regimes. For you unfortunates who, through lack of money or nerve, are unable to rebel, I offer this advice – personalize your uniform.

A Standard Wimp

A Rebel Wimp

Boy Scouts

A normal Boy Scout can be seen on the left.

They are very strange people who spend a lot of time talking about their grunties and fiddling with their woggles.

A genius is not a Boy Scout – he is a Man Scout.
Put your fellow Scouts to shame with your massive WOGGLE.

Question: What do Boy Scouts have that Girl Guides don't?
Answer: Woggles!!

The Heavy Rocker

This is what I would look like if I wasn't a genius. Needless to say, Rockers are pretty brainy.

The True Rebel

Real Genii look like this.

As you have probably already learned from your wide reading and long hours of study in front of the TV – there's money in crime! Lots and lots of lovely cash can be yours if you become a criminal mastermind. There's no need to go robbing banks, etc, you must make the most of your natural surroundings – your school. Remember, you are very lucky to have the chance to swizz such a large number of dumb people who you know will be gathered together in the same place every day. So don't miss this opportunity of a lifetime to set yourself up in style and comfort at the very beginning of your career as a Genius.

Money-making opportunities can be divided into two categories: the Violent and the Non-violent. We'll have the violent things first and then we can calm you down with a bit of non-violence.

Violent Activities

Violence can be a very dangerous thing and because of this most people are terrified by it, especially when it's them being violented! Of course, as a genius I am not moved by these pathetic emotions. If you are going to be any good at violence, you must be afraid neither of dishing it out nor receiving it. Let's begin with some of the gentler threats and their consequences.

Running a Protection Racket

This can be great fun and very profitable. It has two stages:
1. The Threatening
2. The Doing Ghastly Things If the Wimp * Doesn't Pay Up

The threatening stage is probably the most important part of your entire protection racket. If you do this bit correctly, you don't have to do any of the rest. Firstly, single out your prey. If you are amazingly masculine like me it doesn't really matter who you pick on because everyone is probably scared of you. If you are not, pick on someone smaller and weaker than you.

Violence Rule No. 1 – Always pick on wimps.

Method

Grab your victim by the throat. You may now begin your terrifying threats, which will undoubtedly be all the more threatening if you squeeze very hard. Don't overdo this bit though, even if it is extremely enjoyable. Running a protection racket is a crime that will probably go unnoticed by the authorities, but murder is another matter. Allow your victim, say, two days to pay up the sum of £1. You can make this sound a very reasonable proposition by pointing out that by handing over the £1 in question he will be protecting himself from some very nasty consequences indeed.

If he refuses, try an even smaller, younger victim.

Of course, you could genuinely protect someone as their bodyguard. If business gets slow, you can arrange for the victims to be kicked in by a rented bully under your jurisdiction. Then you can clean up by defeating the "bully' in a series of pre-arranged mock-fights.

Dollynapping

Though this is not always violent, you will find that it does involve doing some very nasty things. Little girls, you see, get very attached to their dolls. What you do is kidnap their doll and offer to return it for a small ransom. If the owner refuses to pay up, you can encourage them by cutting off a few of the doll's fingers and toes and sending them through the post – not a very pleasant thing to do, but practical.

Aggro Centres

Pupils very often get highly annoyed by the pressures of school life. Aggravation mounts as uniform, teachers, homework and spots destroy your school mates composure. Which all offers an excellent opportunity for you to make money by setting up "Aggro Centres" to channel off your friend's frustrations.

The most popular model to have in your Aggro Centre is undoubtedly a teacher dummy. You can also have a fellow pupil dummy or anyone else your customers will find annoying. The El Guffo™ dummies currently available are shown below.

Also in the picture you can see some fiendish weapons of torture. Teachers refer to these as "schoolbooks", though we know better, don't we? You may ask why we should have these things in our Aggro Centres. Think again "Schoolbooks" are amazingly popular for ripping up, burning and spitting on.

GARY DOBSON STYLE FLARES

HISTORY
BIOLOGY
GEOGRAPHY
MATHS
ENGLISH
PHYSICS
LATIN
FRENCH
CHEMISTRY

Non-violent Activities

Although non-violent activities can be rather boring, they are undoubtedly safer. Violence draws a lot of attention and so it is wise to have a few unobstrusive schemes up your sleeve.

Gambling

If there is one thing people need after getting up at the crack of dawn to catch the school bus and then working hard for ages without hardly a break, it's stimulating entertainment. The lure of big money, the thrill of the chase, the heart-stopping excitement as you're about to lose the shirt off your back when your chosen runner doesn't win, all this can be provided on a minimum budget if you set up an Insect Racing Track. Insects are quite easily obtained usually at no cost whatsoever. Cockroaches and beetles make the best racers, and spiders are also very good runners (though these may distress some female spectators).

This is what your insect racing track should look like. Remember to charge for every thing – admission, seats, betting slips, standing room, air consumed, no sweets allowed unless bought off you, 50p fine for lack of participation, in fact absolutely anything you want to tax can be taxed.

You can help *your* chosen runner in many ways. This means that you can win lots of money on your no-hope, practically legless brat of an insect whilst your patrons lose pounds which they would otherwise spend on those yummy school dinners. Methods range from the inventive to the downright dishonest.

Here we have an example of genius at its best. Simply sprinkle minute drawing pins over the racing track, then equip your lumbago-diseased, rheumatism-shattered flea with a pair of insect Toughaboots (available from El Guffo™).

Alternatively, you could fence off each lane of your track, saying that this is to avoid the insects attacking each other. Then you fit all your opponents lanes with this electrical mechanism and ZAP all your opponents are eliminated!

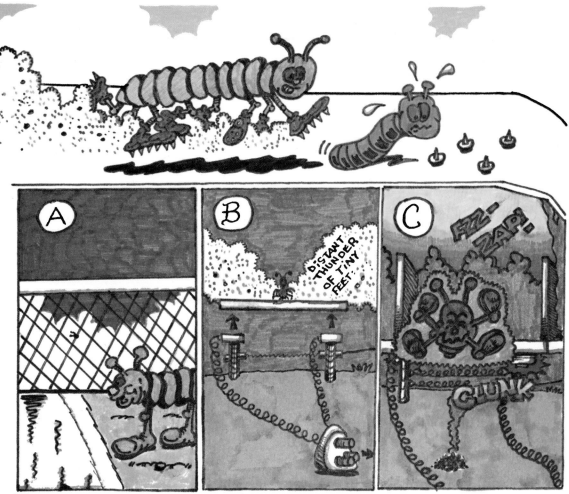

Charity

This is probably the most profitable of my non-violent schemes. One reason for this is that you can do it to teachers – who are rolling in money – without fear of being caught. All you need is a bit of important looking paper like the one below.

Name	Address	Amount paid in £100s £'s pence	
			Thank you for contributing. You have helped save the lives of thousands of innocent head lice who might otherwise become extinct. We hope you will tell your friends of our battle. Thank you once again.

Of course, there are literally hundreds of other moneymaking schemes you could try – mugging, fixing rugby matches, prize fighting, blackmail, book writing – all these are highly immoral and very practical. Which just makes you think, doesn't it? If it wasn't for me, you'd be out there on the street doing all sorts of nasty thing like bullying people and preying on their vices, and not making a penny out of it.

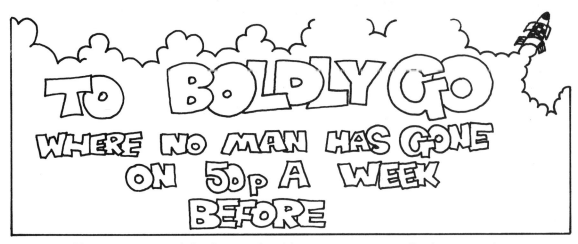

TO BOLDLY GO WHERE NO MAN HAS GONE ON 50p A WEEK BEFORE

Every genius worth his haggis should go to outer space. Such a trip is the ultimate test of endurance, courage, strength, brains and all the other qualities that Deborah Anderson sees in me.

For your trip you must have certain necessities in your suitcase. In fact, you will need several suitcases full of necessities and emergency supplies as well.

Here is my luggage list.

- 25   assorted Y's adorned with rude mottoes.
- 26   Mars bars (one for an emergency).
- 25   pairs of assorted white and fluorescent socks.
- 26   apples (one for an emergency).
- 50   way-out genius-style outfits. It can get a bit boring up there so have some fun dressing up in some new distinctive clothes.
- 90   assorted frozen and liquid haggises (15 for emergencies).
- 300 bottles of whisky (who can live without it?)
- 1   Deborah Anderson (who can live without it?)

As you might have guessed from my luggage list, my voyage was planned to last 25 days. I wasn't just going up there for the fun of it. I planned to leave a multi-purpose satellite up there. This would allow me to phone people up via my ultra-sophisticated satellite and therefore avoid hefty phone bills. Also, by means of the gigantic mirror attached to its side, I can reflect the light of the sun on to the solar receiver on the Genius HQ roof. This means I don't have to pay heating bills either. I can also take my own television films of rugby matches, rock concerts, etc, and relay them to Genius HQ, once again free of charge. Here is what the satellite looks like.

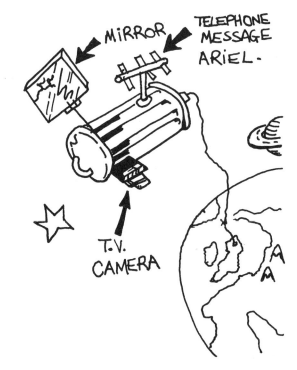

But getting there and back again aren't the only things you will need equipment for. If you are going on a space walk, you will need a space suit. It can be very chilly without one. Seen below is the type I used. This is, without doubt, the most stylish spacesuit in history. Bright and colourful, it also features some ultra-macho studs. All the colours and patterns are so bright and distinctive you might be taken for a star. I often am.

My plans were nearly completed when Deborah Anderson announced her intention to go into orbit with me. ("It'll be so lovely dear. Just you, me and the stars, and the nearest human being hundreds of miles away!") As you might expect, this warranted a few drastic alterations to my carefully laid

To get the satellite up, my amazing resuable rocket was used.

To recharge the engine all you have to do is replace the used aerosols.

plans, eg doubling the rations and providing the sorts of entertainments that Deborah would be accustomed to – washing up, dusting, making beds, that sort of thing. And she had to have a slinky spacesuit made . . .

Hmmm! I might go into space more often.

But despite all this mind-numbing beauty, space is full of danger and to defend yourself and your loved one you will need a weapon. Not just any weapon. If you are going to be able to combat all the horrific nasties you might just find up there, you will need something special – very special. Here it is. El Guffo Industries proudly present (da da da da). . .

The Zappy Gun

(If you are distressed by pictures of fiendish war machines, simply join point A to B and point C to D.)

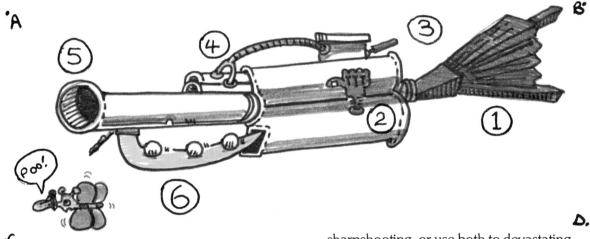

1. These are the bellows. They blow out the ammunition with amazing force.
2. This is the ammo selector. It points to the desired force.
3. This is where your dried peas are kept. Believe me – these are very painful.
4. These barrels are where the peas fly out from. You can fire with one barrel for sharpshooting, or use both to devastating effect.

5. and 6. This is the horrific part of the gun. This is the part that puts the ZAP! into ZAPPY! The little spheres that you can see at the part labelled 6 are in fact **Moth Balls!** Once fired at the unfortunate victim, they are immediately frozen in time as the Moth Ball breaks and releases its fiendish time-preserving vapours.

Surprisingly, being attacked by aliens is by no means the worst ordeal you are likely to encounter in space. In fact, all the really terrible happenings occur in the bathroom. Let's tackle them in order.

After your nutritious breakfast of haggisflakes, with whisky instead of milk, followed by haggis spread on toast, all washed down with a nice mug of hot whisky, the first thing you must do is go to the bathroom. You do this by putting your hand up and saying "please may I go to the bathroom?" This will be met with an ominous silence as Deborah Anderson is busily throwing up all over the window garden after her first encounter with haggisflakes. You may now sneak away quietly before your beloved makes you do the washing up.

As you leave the living room of the spaceship, you will experience a strange rising sensation, and you will notice that your feet are leaving the floor. This is because the living room is the only part of the ship with normal earth gravity and the rest of the ship has no gravity. Either that, or you put too much whisky on your haggisflakes.

Now you float in to the bathroom and soar over to the washbasin. This is where your problems start. You turn on the tap. The water, instead of going into the basin, goes anywhere it wants. To prevent this, keep all your water in Fairy Liquid bottles. Whenever you want to wash, squirt the water into your face, as in Figure 1. It is interesting to note that towels are unnecessary in space, as all the water just floats off.

After washing, you must brush your teeth. This is the quickest way to drive yourself insane. If I was you, I'd take your brush and paste through to the living room, shove it in your gob, then float back quickly to the bathroom.

But washing and brushing your teeth pale into insignificance beside one thing. Going to the Loo. Well, I've said it now. This means the book will be banned from the shelves about three days after publiciation, but who cares? To go comfortably you have to redesign the loo like this.

After spending a total of 15 days in outer space, I suddenly realised that I could no longer stay there. This was because Deborah Anderson, in one of her silly moods, had decided that I was taking far too much whisky on my epic voyage, and so she had only packed 200 bottles instead of the originally planned 300. It was essential that I returned to earth immediately.

Hurriedly I programmed the satellite's computer to follow the correct orbit, then untied the knot that held it to my rocket. As a small punishment, I made Deborah remain on the satellite until I returned.

I landed safely at Genius HQ Mission Control, where I picked up my 100 bottles of whisky. Then, just as I was about to lift off, I heard the phone ringing. I answered it and to my great shock it was Deborah! Some nasty aliens were trying to break into the satellite! They would be inside at any second!

There was not a moment to lose. Within minutes I was streaking towards outer space. As I zoomed towards the besieged satellite, I checked my Zappy Gun. I would need it. The on-board computer beeped and flashed a message – VISUAL CONTACT ESTABLISHED. I looked out of the window. In the distance I could just make out the El Guffo™ symbol on the side of the satellite. Within minutes I was there.

Having no time to put on my spacesuit, I simply pressed the buckle on my G-Man belt which sealed me off from the vacuum by means of a special ray. I drifted across to the satellite and climbed through the airlock. I was in the computer control room. Keeping a sharp lookout for the alien creepies, I sidled over to the ZX81 and punched in a statement in my own secret computer language. Pictures of the interior of my satellite flickered up on the various TV screens. Carefully, I studied each one, but there was no sign of either girlfriend or alien. They must be hiding in one of the blind spots. Suddenly an alarm light flashed silently. There was trouble in the living room. I looked up at the screen that viewed the living area. I was just in time to see a green, scaly hand smother the camera before the screen went blank.

1937 CLOCKWORK
STEAM-POWERED
MODEL MK I

◉ CHANNEL 1

◉ CHANNEL 2

◉ ENGLISH CHANNEL

I went through a moment of panic and fear. Then I brushed it thoughtlessly aside. Deborah was in trouble, there was not a moment to lose.

With mind-blowing speed, I ran through the satellite. I paused at one side of the living room door, listening for a distressing screams from my loved one. There was silence. With no thoughts for my own safety, I swung my foot into the door, effortlessly smashing it open, despite the 2-inch-thick tempered cardboard of which it was made.

I was just about to push the bellows on my Zappy Gun, when I realised just what lay within the room. There were streamers and balloons and confetti all flying around and Adam Dakin was leading the numerous members of the Jason Cowan Fan Club in a rousing chorus of "Happy Birthday To You". Yes, it was my birthday. And I had forgotten. Silly me. Nevertheless, it was very lucky I'd brought that whisky.

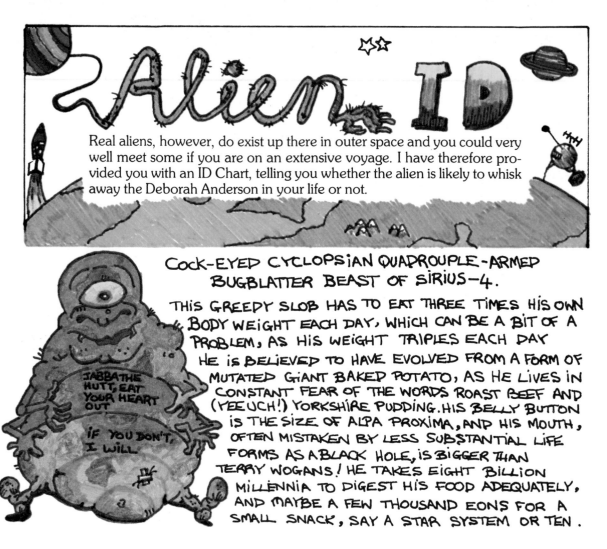

Alien ID

Real aliens, however, do exist up there in outer space and you could very well meet some if you are on an extensive voyage. I have therefore provided you with an ID Chart, telling you whether the alien is likely to whisk away the Deborah Anderson in your life or not.

COCK-EYED CYCLOPSIAN QUADROUPLE-ARMED BUGBLATTER BEAST OF SIRIUS-4.

THIS GREEDY SLOB HAS TO EAT THREE TIMES HIS OWN BODY WEIGHT EACH DAY, WHICH CAN BE A BIT OF A PROBLEM, AS HIS WEIGHT TRIPLES EACH DAY. HE IS BELIEVED TO HAVE EVOLVED FROM A FORM OF MUTATED GIANT BAKED POTATO, AS HE LIVES IN CONSTANT FEAR OF THE WORDS ROAST BEEF AND (YEEUCH!) YORKSHIRE PUDDING. HIS BELLY BUTTON IS THE SIZE OF ALPA PROXIMA, AND HIS MOUTH, OFTEN MISTAKEN BY LESS SUBSTANTIAL LIFE FORMS AS A BLACK HOLE, IS BIGGER THAN TERRY WOGANS! HE TAKES EIGHT BILLION MILLENNIA TO DIGEST HIS FOOD ADEQUATELY, AND MAYBE A FEW THOUSAND EONS FOR A SMALL SNACK, SAY A STAR SYSTEM OR TEN.

JABBA THE HUTT, EAT YOUR HEART OUT

IF YOU DON'T, I WILL

DUCK-BILLED MUCK-FILLED PLATAPUSSY.

THINGUMMYBOBWHATDOYOUCALLEMS OF THE AXEL NEBULA SYSTEM.

THESE CREATURES ARE JUST PLAIN STUPID. THEY JUST DANCE AROUND ALL DAY AND LAUGH. THEY HAVE A LIFECYCLE OF 24 HOURS.

SLOUCH

THE SLOUCH IS CLOSELY RELATED TO THE TERRAN SLOTH, AND IS EQUALLY LAZY. THESE, THOUGH, ARE SLIGHTLY DIFFERENT. THEY HAVE "SLOUCH POUCHES": POCKETS IN THEIR HIPS THEY PUT THEIR PAWS IN. THEY ARE LIKE A PRIMITIVE RACE ON TERRA - THE HOMO SAPIEN, ALSO LAZY, BUT THEIR POCKETS ARE NOT NATURAL FUR OR SKIN TISSUE.

THE WILL-YOU-WON'T YOU OF ALPHA CENTAURI.

THESE CREATURES WREAK HAVOC ALL OVER THE COSMOS, AS WHEN THEY FINALLY BOTH DECIDE TO VOTE, THEY CAN HAVE ONLY ONE VOTE BETWEEN THEM. IT IS HOPED THE GALACTIC HIGH COMMISION WILL MAKE A NEW RULE - ONE VOTE PER BRAIN.

THE MAJORITY OF HEADMASTERS ARE IN FACT, VICIOUS, STUPID ALIEN INFILTRATORS, WHOSE AIM IT IS TO UNDERMINE TERRAN DEFENCES FROM THE INSIDE. THEY SOMETIMES THOUGH, DROP THEIR CAMOUFLAGED GUARD, SHOWING THEIR THEIR TENTACLES AND FORKED TONGUES.

NOTE THE BADLY-CONCEALED TENTACLE.

GREMLIN.

THESE DISGUSTING CREATURES GO AROUND FIDDLING WITH MECHANICAL APPLIANCES, MAKING THINGS GO WRONG AND GENERALLY PUTTING A SPANNER IN THE WORKS. THEY SPECIALISE IN MAKING THINGS GO BUMP IN THE NIGHT AND MAKING SUPERMARKET TROLLEY WHEELS SLIP ALL OVER THE PLACE.

THE DETATCHED TWO-BEDROOM WARBLER.
COMMONLY KNOWN AS THE DORMOBILE OF URSA MINOR

THIS CREATURE IS CLOSELY RELATED TO THE TERRAN SNAIL, BUT ARE SLIGHTLY MORE ADVANCED. THEY TOO HAVE THEIR HOUSES ON THEIR BACKS, STONE, WITH DOUBLE GLAZING AND CENTRAL HEATING AND FITTED WALL-TO-WALL CARPETS.

War is a subject that is always in the news, and even if the big one does not occur, you will find it extremely useful to have a private army. If can be used for so many things – releasing pent-up aggression, making loud bangs and spectacular explosions, weeding the Genius HQ garden, or maybe even saving the world from destruction.

RECRUITMENT

If you are going to have an army that deserves a genius commander like you, you will need to select your soldiers very carefully. They must have at least a glimmer of intelligence, they must be able to survive on a daily diet of haggis, and they must never drink more than 10 bottles of whisky a day. As you can see, a genius's soldiers are no ordinary men. Did you think they would be?

Sadly, people with all these qualities are almost always intelligent as well, which means they have enough sense not to join up. For this reason it is necessary to employ a method of persuasion that has stood up well to the test of time. It is called PRESS-GANGING.

To do this you will need: 1. A 3:1 ratio on your side
2. A cudgel
3. A stretcher

Your Press Gang   If these guys are on your side, that's fine. If not – run!

Your Target

You must choose your target very carefully. Your perfect fall-guy must be good enough to be in your army, but not so good that he can overpower your press gang.

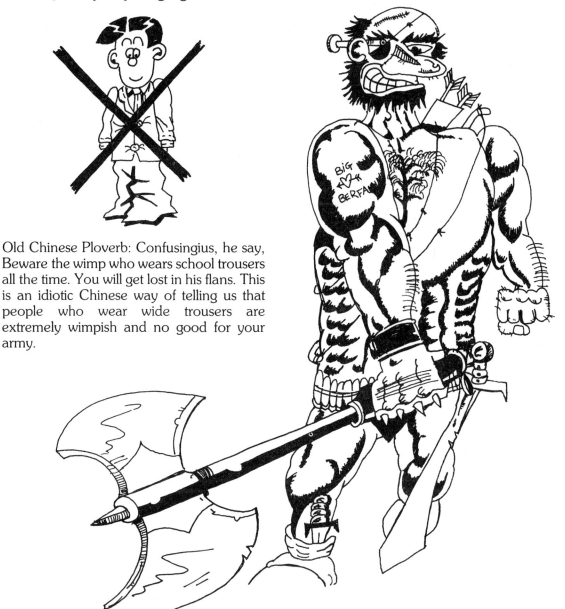

Old Chinese Ploverb: Confusingius, he say, Beware the wimp who wears school trousers all the time. You will get lost in his flans. This is an idiotic Chinese way of telling us that people who wear wide trousers are extremely wimpish and no good for your army.

Definitely Not. I don't even dare draw a cross through this picture. Old Chinese Ploverb; Confusingius, he say Use your common breeding sense!

The Method

Once you have chosen your victim, you may begin what is known as "the mugging procedure." Get your gang to leap out of some handy shadows on to the defenseless victim. Once you have overpowered him, give him a good knock on the head with your cudgel. Then you can easily ease the unconscious recruit on to the stretcher. Now ferry him home and set off again to pick up the next one.

TRAINING

Once this part of your project is completed, you can start training your recruits. Having kitted them out in a uniform, you will give them their first glimpse of the assault course. Before their first attempt at this be sure to strip them of any equipment or clothing that could be damaged, and then make them tackle the course without a word of advice from you.

The Assault Course

Here follows a suitably terrifying assault course.

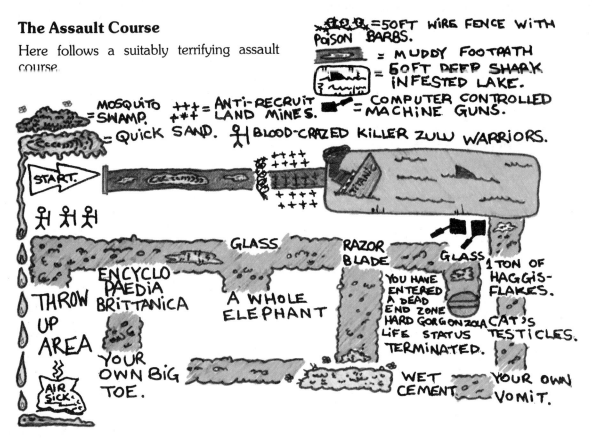

= MOSQUITO SWAMP.

+++ = ANTI-RECRUIT LAND MINES.

= QUICK SAND.

= 50FT WIRE FENCE WITH POISON BARBS.

= MUDDY FOOTPATH

= 50FT DEEP SHARK INFESTED LAKE.

= COMPUTER CONTROLLED MACHINE GUNS.

= BLOOD-CRAZED KILLER ZULU WARRIORS.

START.

THROW UP AREA

AIR SICK

ENCYCLOPAEDIA BRITTANICA

YOUR OWN BIG TOE.

GLASS

A WHOLE ELEPHANT

RAZOR BLADE

GLASS

YOU HAVE ENTERED A DEAD END ZONE HARD GORGONZOLA LIFE STATUS TERMINATED.

1 TON OF HAGGIS-FLAKES.

CAT'S TESTICLES.

WET CEMENT

YOUR OWN VOMIT.

Before your brave recruits set off, it is wise to program your computers to **narrowly** miss them. And you can disable your Zulu warriors by keeping them on a strict carrot juice diet. These precautions will prolong the lives of your soldiers, but the overall effect will be more than enough to give them a major attack of the trembles. Have seriously injured recruits sent round to the local butcher, and introduce the rest of them to their next ordeal – the Firing Range.

It is as you announce that they have by no means completed their course that you will notice how extremely annoyed they are. You can combat this by presenting all those who completed the assault course with little plastic or papier maché badges like this.

I'M REALLY
— MACHO —
I COMPLETED
A REALLY
GRUELLING
ASSAULT
COURSE!

HE WHO CHEATS WINS

The Firing Range

SOAP

Dead simple you might think. But all is not what it seems. The targets are, in fact, cardboard cutouts. The real things are hiding in the bushes behind the recruits ready to rush out at your signal. The guns fire black puddings. For this reason it is called a Bluchy Gun. When armed with these, your army will become an indomitable force, worthy of the greatest opponents. Like the Argentinians? Read on . . .

HOW WE DID IT

Gripping stuff, eh? Obviously the Argies had retreated as soon as were sighted.

The success of this operation was greatly helped by my Genius war equipment. The following are a selection from the El Guffo ™ Mail Order Weapons Catalogue (all nationalities catered for, payment 90 days in advance of delivery in unused Scottish pound notes). Arms dealing can be a profitable sideline of your private army.

THE PUDDING PELTER

This gun is filled with disgusting black pudding mixture at hole number 1. No one is very sure what black puddings are made of, though rumours of minced slugs, concentrated beetles brains and dehydrated lice abound. You can try any of these, and mixtures are exceptionally effective. It is a good idea to make mixture mixing a punishment for your army.

The mixture flows along the gun and into the pudshaper, marked 2 on the diagram. It is here that it gains its characteristic pudding shape. The puddings are stored in the pudshaper until the trigger is pulled, when they are pumped out at hole number 3.

The pudding pelter is a hideous weapon. It takes a genius to handle something like this.

THE GENIUS MULTI-PURPOSE WARMOBILE

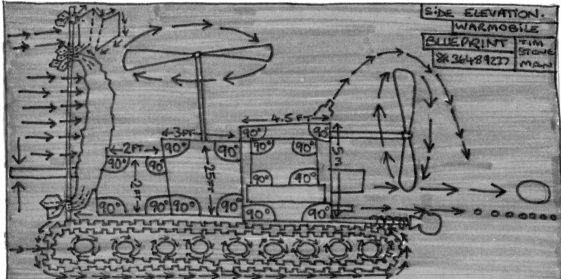

El Guffo certainly know their business. They know that many of you budding army commanders won't have enough money to buy ships, tanks and aeroplanes separately, so they've squashed them all together in one heap. This complex bit of machinery has controls that are so simple even a baby could operate if (please try to fill in the order form with joined up writing, though).

OUR GENIUS MULTI-PURPOSE WARMOBILE KIT CONSISTS OF THE DETAILED BLUE PRINT SHOWN BELOW, LEFT. PLEASE FOLLOW THE DIAGRAM CAREFULLY.

YOUR FINISHED WEAPON WILL LOOK SOMETHING LIKE THIS...

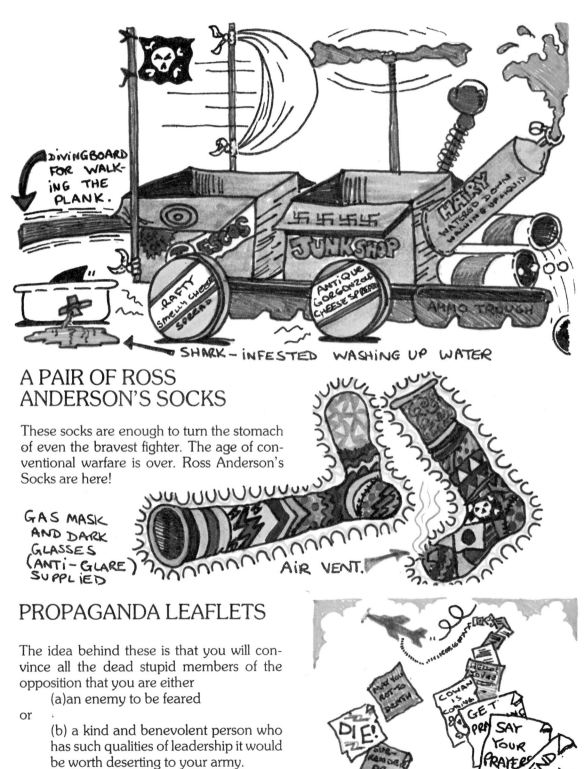

DIVINGBOARD FOR WALKING THE PLANK.

SHARK-INFESTED WASHING UP WATER

A PAIR OF ROSS ANDERSON'S SOCKS

These socks are enough to turn the stomach of even the bravest fighter. The age of conventional warfare is over. Ross Anderson's Socks are here!

GAS MASK AND DARK GLASSES (ANTI-GLARE) SUPPLIED

AIR VENT.

PROPAGANDA LEAFLETS

The idea behind these is that you will convince all the dead stupid members of the opposition that you are either

    (a) an enemy to be feared

or

    (b) a kind and benevolent person who has such qualities of leadership it would be worth deserting to your army.

This method of warfare is cheating, cowardly and and immoral.
What's more, it works.

CAREERS FOR GENII

Every budding genius wants to be rich, famous and successful when he grows up. It is important to choose your field of excellence early in life so that you're always ahead of the opposition. Being a multiple genius I have already started on several careers.

THE FREUCHE BUGLE

COWAN ~
Investigative Journalist

Here follows my in depth report on dark doings in the streets of Freuchie on Tuesday nights.

WHAT DO GIRL GUIDES DO IN THE DARK?

by Jason Cowan, Star Reporter

The moon is full. Clouds, however, hide it and pour down icy rain. The wind charges down the empty, boarded up street. I can only wish that I hadn't been chosen for this most hideous of assignments. For tonight . . . the Girl Guides are about!

The windows of the houses are closely curtained. Horseshoes are hung on every door. Crucifixes are hung above the horse-shoes. These are quaint local customs which are carried out every Tuesday night in this bleak, remote village. The origin of the custom is lost in the mists of time, but is it just coincidence that Guides are held every Tuesday night?

Faces peer anxiously at me through the letter boxes. Is my disguise unsatisfactory? Are they wary of my tartan cape and dark glasses? I do not care and drink some more whisky to give me courage. I shuffle on, braving the wind and rain and hail and think that I shall write in rhyme the remainder of my tale:

WHAT GIRL GUIDES DAE IN THE DARK
(A SCOTTISH POEM)

I walked aroond the corner
On the dark and stormy nicht,
An' the moon came oot 'tween the cloods
An' 'bliged me wi' some licht.
My tartan cloak flapped noisily,
The wind it fairly blew,
But doon the street I spied a lass
Distinctly dressed in blue!

This was, withoot a shade of doobt,
The kind for which I searched –
A girl guide, that fearsome beastie
An' she was heading for the kirk*.
Noiselessly, I followed her
An' tiptoed doon the street.
I took a short cut tae the kirk,
Hopin' that's where they'd meet.

Alas, the kirk was empty,
So I hid an' hoped a girl
Would make her way tae guides
An' the witch in charge, Black Owl.
In time my prayer was answered,
A lass, thin, dark and tall –
A local lass named Jackie –
She went into the church hall.

For a time I did not follow.
The encounter had been a shock!
How many more people I knew
Upon the hall door would knock?
After a while I reasoned
That Jackie had been the last
So I climbed up tae a window
And peered in through the glass.

Within I saw a sight
To stir the strongest hearts,
The lassies o' the village
Were all dolled up, the tarts!
I was aboot tae shoot oot "Cor!"
When I saw Black Owl – what a lark!
Lookin' like the divil, she wis
And wis holdin' a toastin' fork!

The guides looked like they wis leavin',
And wi' the Black Owl at their head
They a' trooped oot o' the hall
And almost scared me dead.
I hid mysel' just in time,
they didnae see, thank the Lord,
I hate tae think what they would ha' done
If they knew they were bein' followed.

They walked through the night fer miles,
An' noiser than 40 buses,
Surely this wis nae the sort o' thing
To teach the poor wee lasses.
Ne'ertheless, on they walked
To a Godforsaken spot,
The moon was hidden by the bare twisted trees
Whose branches were nothing but rot.

So this was the place where the rituals were held,
An evil, poisonous site.
'Tis true, they must hae been foul o' mind
To go oot on such a bad night.
They a' lit fires and sang and danced
Aroond them 'till they were tired,
Then they took oot their muckle* great toastin' forks
And cooked some strange meat on the fire.

What was the strange food that they cooked then ate?
Was it Brain cakes, Black Pud, Calf's head?
Did they go oot an' mug poor grannies at night
Then make sausagemeat o' the dead?
It was as I was watching this divilish feast
That I got the greatest shock o' me life,
A guide had been sentry and seen me hide
An' now threatened me wi' a knife.

Withoot any protest I went tae Black Owl
(My grunties were at risk, ye see).
She said "silly laddie, whit were ye doin'?"
To which I replied "you're askin' me?
Ye terrorize the village at the dead o' nicht,
Ye mack mair noise than 50 bulls seein' red.
Ye eat unknown fleshing, roasted by the fire,
Do ye think I could join ye?" I said.
An' so a great time wis had by a', (Especially me o' course),
The guides were havin' a sausage sizzle,
The meat was neither granny nor horse.

The moral o' this story,
If you a journalist would be,
Is never do yer stuff in rhyme
(I got sacked for this muck).

*Kirk = Church
*Muckle = big

45

The Home Economics teacher has no idea that I am, in fact, a creative chef without equal. Don't laugh! All the best cooks are men, and my *Cuisine El Guffo*™ is very macho! If you don't believe me, try the following menu. I hereby do swear that every recipe that follows is totally genuine and will work.

BANQUET FOR A GENIUS

Starter

BRAINS ON TOAST

You will need:

- [ ] 1 sheep's head
- [ ] 1 egg
- [ ] 2 teaspoons breadcrumbs
- [ ] ½ teaspoon salt
- [ ] ½ teaspoon pepper
- [ ] 1 tablespoon chopped parsley
- [ ] A little grated lemon rind
- [ ] Some boiling fat

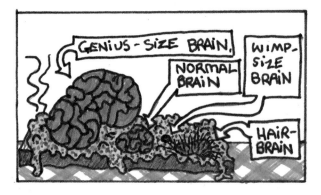

Remove brains from sheep's head. Wash in lemon and water. Put into boiling water for ten minutes, then drain. Beat lightly with a fork in a basin. Add egg, breadcrumbs, salt, pepper, parsley and lemon rind. Dip an iron spoon into the boiling fat and take up a small portion of the mouthwatering mixture and drop into the fat. If too light they will puff up (though *you* are more likely to throw up). To stop this add more breadcrumbs, then cook the remaining mixture for 3 to 5 minutes. Drain on kitchen paper (loo paper is just as effective) and serve on toast.

Main Course

BOILED CALF'S HEAD

You will need:

- [ ] ½ or whole calf's head
- [ ] 1 tablespoon salt
- [ ] 1 plate raw vegetables
- [ ] Parsley sauce

Clean the calf's head. Then, by means of a pointed knife, remove all the bones and also the brains. Roll up the head lengthwise in the form of a galantine. Fasten it up in a clean buttered cloth and bind it with a piece of tape to keep it in good shape. Put it in a saucepan with cold water to cover. Add salt and vegetables. Bring to the boil, skim, and cover the pan with the lid. Continue boiling for 3½ hours, according to size.

Then take it up and remove the cloth. Place the head on a hot dish. Prepare a good parsley sauce and add the calf's brains, previously blanched and cut up into little dice shapes. Crimp the ears by cutting with scissors; skin the tongue and place beside the head. Pour over the sauce and serve very hot.

Pudding

SCOTCH MIST
(A pretty doss*thing actually)

You will need:

- [ ] 12 macaroons
- [ ] 6 sponge fingers
- [ ] ¾ pint cream
- [ ] Pink and green colouring
- [ ] As much whisky as you like

Crush your macaroons and fingers. Place in bowl with some whisky and half the cream. Mix to a stiff paste and put into a glass or silver dish, heaped into a pyramid. Whisk the remainder of the cream with a little sugar and divide in half. Colour one half pink and the other half green. Put a good tablespoon of each colour into forcing bags and decorate pyramid according to turn-on.

* doss = fantastic, marvellous, fabulous, not bad.

Drinks to Complement the Meal

SEMI-ALCOHOLIC NETTLE BEER
(even better when made with Scottish nettles)

You will need:

- [ ] 2 lb nettles
- [ ] Handful of dandelions
- [ ] Brown sugar to taste
- [ ] ½ oz yeast
- [ ] 1 teaspoon ginger

The main advantage of this drink is that it only takes 27 hours to mature. And it makes a nice change from whisky. Wash herbs and put into a pan with enough water to cover. Boil for about 20 minutes. Strain, sweeten and, if too strong (unlikely if you're Scottish) dilute with cold water. When almost cold add the yeast and ginger. Let it "work" for about 3 hours. When all has risen, skim off the top. Put into dry, clean, screw-topped bottles and leave for 24 hours before drinking. Store in a cool place.

NON-ALCOHOLIC OATMEAL WATER
(for when you're on the wagon)

You will need:

- [ ] 3 quarts water
- [ ] ¼ lb oatmeal
- [ ] 1½ oz sugar

Boil all the ingredients for about ¾ hour. Do not strain. Shake well before drinking. Dilute to taste.

In summer, after violent excercise such as Grand Prix Walking and Big Fly Hunting, this drink is pretty doss when cold. Can be taken hot in winter.

Of course, what you'll all be saying to yourselves now is: "If he's so clever, why aren't governments all over the world clamouring for his services as a secret agent?" Unfortunately, owing to the Official Secrets Act, I am unable to reveal the real nature of my activities in this field. I will just say that I am in the employ of certain governments, in what capacity you will have to guess.

In fact, being a secret agent is one of of the best bits of being a genius: delivering secret messages, stealing top secret plans, blowing things up — yes, it's a great life in the SS. Another advantage of being a spy, as you have probably noticed from the films, is that you get to meet plenty of GIRLS.

EQUIPMENT

There are certain indispensible items of equipment you will need before embarking on this career.

YET ANOTHER El Guffo™ WONDERMOBILE

I think we can safely say that this is *this ultimate in pedal cars.* Accessories include: a pudding proof shield; a periscope (the car is submersible); a few machine guns; a pair of wings (it's *supposed* to fly as well).

Unfortunately, the weight of the machine guns and things means that it can't leave the ground as a plane, and it sinks to the seas's bottom as a submarine. However, these teething problems have been overcome by the springs which can get it into the air and off the sea bed (for a second or two at any rate).

SOME LITTLE EXTRAS

Sadly, you can't spend all your days as a spy zooming around in a pedal car. Every genius secret agent must carry bits of genius equipment on his person.

How about a **Sellotape Dispenser Watch?** Very useful for sticking bombs on walls, cars, etc, or for taping up the mouths of kidnapped generals.

Even this device isn't half as good as the **Limpet Button Mine** (though it is wise to sellotape the mines on to whatever is being blown up rather than relying on the little sucker at the back of the button). Having only a discreet 15 cm diameter, you can see that these buttons are capable of giving out enormous explosive power!

But what if you are searched? Weapons like these will probably be discovered by the enemy, despite being disguised as everyday objects. The only way to get round this problem is to disguise your spying aids, not only as everyday objects but as actual parts of your body that are not likely to be removed in a strip search. **The Glove Gun** is an excellent example of this type of aid.

The nails are deadly. They're tipped with a terrible poison which can be shot out like bullets when the squeeze trigger is used. And the trigger can be hidden, and discreetly squeezed in your pocket. Now all you have to do is ask yourself what you're supposed to do with the trigger when you're searched. Answers should be in joined up writing and sent to the Jason Cowan Fan Club.

But I must stop disclosing the details of my top-secret equipment. Are you trustworthy? Yes? How do I know that?

Anyway, who needs equipment when you've got that most important thing — technique? Technique, as it relates to the secret agent, means being able to hit people. You can gain experience by joining up with the local branch of the Genius Private Army. However, in the subtle business of espionage pud-pelters and warmobiles are rarely of use. You will need to cultivate your hand-to-hand fighting techniques. This is how it is done.

1. THE HAKISOKIT

This is a particularly lethal move for knocking out two attackers at once.

2. THE SOTTI GLOCKINGOC-KIVIKILUCKY QUADIFOUR POINT PINC-PUNCH

This is a quick, no-hassle way of eliminating four opponents. You can knock out six by

using the HAKISOKIT when you land.

But what if all your limbs are unavailable? Here we must revert to daft things that are bad for us. Things to be used sparingly. Things that work.

3. THE CRANIUM SMASH

This here's for the cranium abusers. This one's pretty desperate. It's merely a case of hit as hard as you can and the one with the hardest nut survives. The author accepts no responsibility for fatalities that may occur during the use of this counter-attack.

Actually, if you're a good secret agent you won't have to fight. A good spy does his job so well that he is never caught and so never gets in a fight. One of the many difficult duties a spy has is delivering secret messages. It is extremely important that you are not caught with these in your possession as they normally contain Top Secret things that the enemy must never see. So how do you prevent them from falling into enemy hands? Well, it's no good walking around with a suitcase full of vital papers handcuffed to your wrist. That's a bit obvious. Instead try this.

A bit painful perhaps, but all in the course of duty.

DISGUISES

Totally change your appearance for minimum cost and maximum effect.

BEFORE   AFTER

1) USE TOILET ROLL FOR NOSE, MARGARINE CARTON LIDS FOR EARS, ASSORTED MOPS AND BROOMS FOR HAIR AND MOUSTACHE.

BEFORE   AFTER

2) SIMPLY USE OLD STOCKINGS OR TIGHTS.

BEFORE   AFTER

3) RAID MA'S DRESSING TABLE.

49

WORLD DO

BOARD GAME FOR 2 OR

START HERE

FOLLOW THE YELLOW BRICK ROAD.

TO CONQUER THE WORLD YOU WILL NEED: A DICE, A COUNTER FOR EACH PLAYER, LUCK & DETERMINATION

YOU GET DRESSED UP IN A MILITARY UNIFORM. MOVE UP TWO PLACES FOR HAVING A BIT OF SENSE.

YOU MEET A DRUNKEN NEAN-DETHAL IN THE STREET. IT'S CAVE MAN! YOUR ARMY HAS BEEN STARTED

THE RUGGER TEAM FOOLISH VOLUNTEERS TO JOIN YOUR ARMY. MISS A TURN TO PRO-VIDE A UNIFORM UNLESS YOU CAN THROW A SIX.

17 YOU BLOW UP THE HOUSES OF PARLIAMENT, THE WHITE HOUSE, AND THE KREM-LIN. THE WORLD-WIDE PUBLIC IS ETERNALLY GRATEFUL, AND ALL JOIN UP WITH THE ARMY. GO ON THREE SQUARES.

16 YOUR ARMY IS NOW PRE-PARED TO TAKE ON THE WORLD MISS A TURN

YOU LIE LOW FOR SIX MONTHS TO AVOID THE POLICE, AND TO TRAIN YOUR POLICE TO BE GENII. MISS A TURN.

YOU ROB A BANK TO PRO-VIDE MONEY FOR A WAR-MOBILE THE POLICE HAVE NO EVIDENCE.

13 PAUSE FOR A CUP OF TEA. MOVE ON ONE SQUARE.

PIGGY BANK

NO CHEATING BIG BROTHER IS WATCHING YOU

18 DEBORAH ANDERSON DECIDES THAT THE MILITARY LIFE IS NOT FOR HER, AND LEAVES YOU. THIS IS GREAT NEWS-YOU WERE GETTING SICK OF HER ANYWAY! MISS A TURN LOOK-ING FOR A NEW GIRL-FRIEND.

19 TO FIND YOUR GIRLFRIEND YOU MUST KISS EVERY FEMALE IN THE ROOM. (YES, EVEN HER!) NOW CHOOSE THE BEST.

20 YOU ARE UNABLE TO PROVIDE FOOD FOR THE WORLD PUBLIC. EVERYONE LEAVES EXCEPT THE OR-IGINAL MEMBERS.

21 YOU BUILD A MASSIVE HAGGIS FLAKES FACTORY TO PROVIDE FOOD FOR THE WORLD PUBLIC. IF THEY HAVE LEFT YOU, THEY RETURN TO YOU. IF NOT, THEY ARE SICK.

24 DEBORAH GETS BORED WITH CIVILLIAN LIFE. RETURN TO SQUARE SIX.

23 DEBORAH ANDERSON DISCOVERS THE IDENTITY OF YOUR REPLACEMENT GIRLFRIEND. (FOLLOW THE INSTRUCTIONS ON SQUARE EIGHTEEN)

22 THE WORLD POPULATION DESPISE HAGGIS FLAKES THEY GO OFF AND START THEIR OWN ARMY.

25 YOU HIRE A CROP SPRAYER AND BRING THE COUNTRY TO I KNEES BY SPRAYI IT WITH YOUR BODY BUILDING MEAL. MOVE ON 2 SQUAR

50

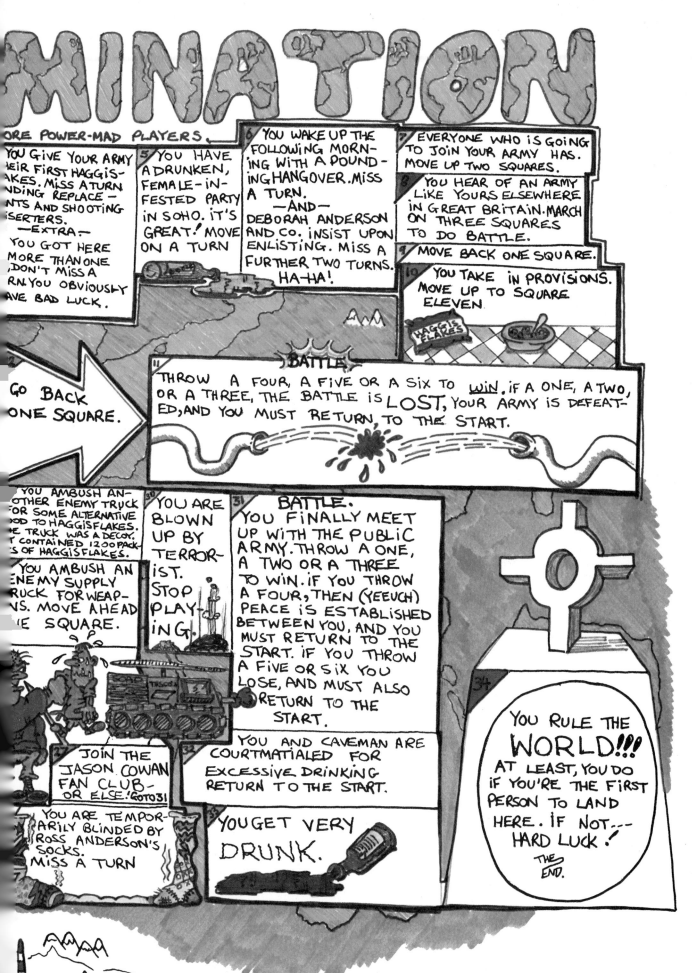

All work and no play makes for dull genii, and so every budding genius should take up some sort of sporting activity to show that he is a well-rounded person. Whatever sport you choose there's one Golden Rule that you have to remember –

Never mind about playing the game
The only thing that matters is WINNING.

HOW TO WIN AT GRAND PRIX WALKING

Take walking, for example. Walking is something we all take for granted, we do it everyday whether we like it or not. But did you know that Grand Prix walking is regarded as a serious sport in some circles? Not many people do. That's why it's a good sport for geniuses to take up – there's not much competition! It's not like marathon running, where you have to beat half the bloody town and Jimmy Saville!

You'll need to put in a bit of training if you're going to reach competition standard. Why not start tomorrow? Get up early and put on your walking shoes (and your clothes if you don't want to get arrested) and start practising your walking technique. Although training can be done indoors on wet, cold or generally nasty days, there is more scope if you practice outside. This is what you do:

1. Stand with your feet together.
2. Move your right foot forward.
3. Place it on the ground in front of you.
4. Bring your left foot forward and put it on the ground in front of your right foot.

Repeat these movements in the correct order and you can't go wrong. When you have exercised in this way for a few minutes, go back to bed for a rest.

A few days of this and you will be up to competition standard. As I mentioned earlier, not many people know about Grand Prix Walking, so if you're lucky you'll be the only one to turn up for the race and will be acclaimed the winner without having to take a step.

If by some unlucky chance some other idiots turn up for the race they can easily be beaten with Cowan's brilliantly conceived Winning Strategy:

> Get out of sight of the other competitors as soon as possible and then, when no one can see you, start RUNNING! They'll never keep up with you no matter how fast they walk. Start walking again when you're in sight of the winning post.

HOW TO CATCH A FISH
ON 50P A WEEK.

I once started to write a book called "The Failing Fisherman's Handbook." I was just the right person to write it. Three years fishing and I'd never caught a thing. Nevertheless it was a pretty good book, packed with useful advice like not to sit on a rod rest unless you want to change your hobby to ornithology, and reminding you that knee-high water is quite safe as long as you don't stand on your head.

I would spend hours on the riverbank, braving the elements in a blue kagool, and making great leaps in the science of fishing. I had tried insects, worms, fish fingers, Celtic supporters, just about everything as bait but I still hadn't caught a thing. Then it suddenly dawned on the Genius brain, what I needed to do was get down there with them, Underwater Fishing was the way to catch those slippery creatures of the deep. Not only Underwater Fishing, but Night Underwater Fishing! I'd catch them when they were snoozing.

Under cover of darkness, clad in wet suit and snorkel, my trusty harpoon gun in my hand, I slipped out of the house and made my way to the unwelcoming loch. I slid into the cold green water and pushed my way through the long thin weeds. Suddenly a menacing shadow loomed ahead. It surged through the water at incredible speed, making a bee-line for my handsome features. My fingers tightened on the trigger of my harpoon gun. But I was too late. I could not believe its power and strength as it almost burst through my face plate, with jaws gaping. I could not help but scream inwardly. With rippling muscles I extricated the snorkel from down my throat. I screamed outwardly.

The hideous fish circled round and prepared for another attack. Hand to hand combat was the only answer. I thrashed at the water with my snorkel, raining blows on the bloodthirsty behemoth of the loch.

"Jaaaason! What the hell are you doing in the garden pond at this time of night?! You'll frighten the goldfish!"

The man was wrong. I'd killed it! Bertram the Great White Goldfish was finally conquered. An amazing achievement on 50p a week. (Actually it cost a bit more than that because Dad stopped my pocket money for two weeks **and** made me buy another goldfish.)

30-PIECE ORCHESTRA PLAYING "JAWS".

DA-DUM- DA-DUM DA-DUM DA DA DA DA

MISSED!

WET SUIT (WELL, DAD'S SUIT IS BOUND TO GET WET UNDERWATER).

JELLYFISH.

HORSE-RIDING FOR GENII

You may think horse riding is strictly for the birds, and I have to admit that you see more girls astride those great galloping beasts than you do geniuses, but, believe it or not, this Great Genius was once a talented horseman. Every Sunday I would don the traditional costume of the horse and hound brigade and go down to the stables clutching several 50ps to pay for an hour of brisk trotting round the Scottish countryside.

Of course, when I first started I didn't get much trotting into that hour, but I got a lot of lying on my back with my legs in the air. I seemed to have trouble getting on the horse. I put it all down to the weather. You see, I started riding in the depths of a Scottish winter. "Wrap up well," said my thoughtful mother, so I would set out wearing two vests, two pairs of pants, three pairs of socks, a shirt, a thick woollen jumper, a pair of wellies, a body warmer, an anorak and a kagool. You

see my problem? I eventually decided that the only way I would get on the horse's back was to take all my clothes off, mount the horse, and put them all back on again. The trouble was, as soon as I got on the horse's back, the damn thing would take off like a bleeding rocket. I got nicked six times for exposing myself and distressing the public. I certainly suffered from exposure, but "distressing the public", my big toe! They were rolling around in the streets in hysterics! By the sixth time they had set up chairs in the street and were charging ten pence a seat.

There had to be an easier way of getting on a horse. There was. I invested in a Gettingonahorser. To mount, you lay the Gettingonahorser against the side of the horse, then place one foot on the bottom rung, and the other foot on the next rung, and so on, until you reach either the horse's back or the end of the Gettingonahorser. I tried this. Guess what. It didn't work. As soon as I laid the thing on the horse's side, and put both feet on the proper rungs, the bloody horse ran

GETTING ONAHORSER

off! There I was lying on my back with my legs in the air again.

Summer came at last, and stripped to only jeans and a T shirt, I did it at last. I actually got on a horse. "Now when you want him to stop," said the teacher, "tap him gently with both feet and pull gently on the reins." So the Great Genius went galloping off through a great big field. He pulled gently on the reins and tapped the horse gently with his feet. The stupid horse hadn't listened to the teacher; it increased its speed to 30 mph. Luckily, at the bottom of the field was a 6 foot hedge. He'll have to stop there, said the Genius. The horse thought it was lucky too. He was an old hunter.

"STOP!" I yelled. "YOU STUPID BLOODY BEAST, there's a 6 foot hedge and you're going straight for iiiiiiiiiittttttttttt!!?"

With great presence of mind, the Genius jumped off. I am searching for my right wellie to this day. I think I left it in the hedge . . . if you find it send it to the usual address.

56

ARE YOU REALLY VILE IN APPEARANCE?

Are you ashamed to go out in public?

THEN El Guffo's Mail Order requisites are for you.
Send now for our all colour brochure.

Or you could just pop into your
local chemist (if you're brave
enough to go out!)

We stock:

Dandruff Shampoo

Acne Lotion

Breath Freshener

Anti-perspirant Deodorants

False Teeth Adhesive

Hair Removing Creme

Hair Restorer

Corn Plasters

Odour Eaters

Ear Wax Remover

Eye wash for Bloodshot Eyes

Smoker's Toothpaste

Slimmer's Biscuits

Anti Bedwetting Tablets

Sweets for stuffy Noses

Hankies for Runny Noses

Mouthwash for Bad Breath

57

The life of a genius is a lonely one. He spends all his time building things, knocking things down, and chasing after girls. Some genii are so absorbed by their hobbies and strange projects, and so short of the 50p's needed to carry them out, that they are prepared to do almost anything to make money, as long as it's not WORK.

Anyway, for the work-shy-genius, here is a way for you to discover a fortune in ancient 24-carat gold rings pulls. These are all that remain of the ancient beer cans that were part of the alcohol collection amassed by one King Jock. The King's Druid, recognising the value of the cans, collected the ring pulls as they were thrown away by the drunken monarch. The Druid took his ring pull collection to a remote spot, where he created a palace to house it. The building was made mostly of wood, only the door frames and underground passages being built of stone. He also conjured up an army of immortal monsters to guard the treasure from thieves.

As time went by, the palace rotted and fell to bits, leaving only the stone doorframes. The entrances and the exits to the underground treasure vaults were blocked and concealed by the elements and nature.

Somewhere in Great Britain a fortune in beer can rings pulls waits to be discovered. To locate this treasure you must use the clues in the passage you have just read and in this ancient manuscript (which was unearthed during recent excavations behind the music hut at Bell Baxter High School). *Good luck!*

OTHAN'S QUEST

He moved through the forest without a sound.
He was Othan, Othan the Stalker, Othan the Warrior,
Othan the Thief.
He unslung the magic stone from around his neck.
It twirled and spun on its chain and pointed South.
He journeyed. He journeyed South for many days.
Until at last he saw the bare door frames straight ahead.

Othan approached the circle of door frames.
He walked into the middle of the circle and found the
centre.
He dug and scraped with his bare hands.
As the sun downed in the evening sky a stone trapdoor
was revealed.
Othan heaved at the metal ring.
Slowly the trapdoor opened and Othan descended.

The trapdoor shut above him.
And his world became darkness.
Afraid, he walked down steps he could not see.
At the bottom there was light.
He entered a passage with torches blazing on the
stone walls.

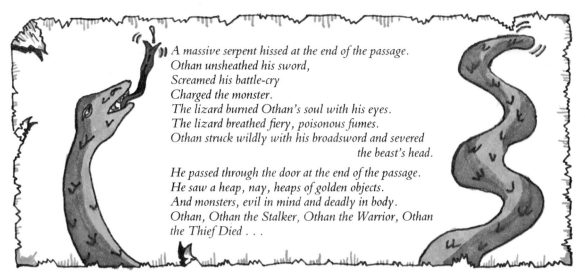

A massive serpent hissed at the end of the passage.
Othan unsheathed his sword,
Screamed his battle-cry
Charged the monster.
The lizard burned Othan's soul with his eyes.
The lizard breathed fiery, poisonous fumes.
Othan struck wildly with his broadsword and severed
                                        the beast's head.

He passed through the door at the end of the passage.
He saw a heap, nay, heaps of golden objects.
And monsters, evil in mind and deadly in body.
Othan, Othan the Stalker, Othan the Warrior, Othan
the Thief Died . . .

So there you are! But please remember, it is an offence to desecrate Ancient Monuments. We can't have every idiot with a spade digging over the nation's heritage — even if the treasure turns out to be in England.

For this reason, only Official Questors will be allowed to take part in the search. Official Questors will dress in the leather 'n' studs Barbarian costume, modelled here by G-Man.

To make your outfit, you will need:
    A bearskin
    A dead cow
    Some studs
    Your old Santa Claus beard

First, take your bearskin and rip it up into loincloth shape. Don't worry about the ragged edges, they help give it that rugged Barbarian look.

Now we move on to the dead cow, pausing only to throw up in a convenient corner. With a nice sharp knife, skin the cow. If it's a young one, save the head to make boiled calf's head (see page 46). Cure the skin and cut the resulting leather into the correct pattern for a jerkin, belt and a pair of boots. Sew all the bits together, bash some studs in and their you are! And just to complete the outfit, put on your Santa Claus beard.

Sadly, the double headed battleaxe is unavailable from El Guffo's ordering service,

but you can make your own by following the simple instructions in *Blue Peter Annual Number 10.*

Here, Deborah models the lady Barbarian outfit.

And, lastly some final clues to the whereabouts of the valuable ring pulls.
1. They are not in my bedroom.
2. Nor are they in my back garden.
3. Or in Deborah Anderson's bedroom.
4. And not in her back garden either.

INDEX

Mc Mac

WOT! NO MACS!
AH, YES!

I know you're out there fans!
NOW is your chance to worship your ultimate man and sex object
NOW is your chance to recognize true genius
NOW is your chance to contribute to the coffers of the best-selling author
the world has ever known

—————————— **YES** ——————————
JOIN THE

NOW

while stocks of my pukey, amazingly cheap, made-in-Taiwan badges and
wallets and things last. (Admittedly I've seen better things to come out of
my toilet. Come to think of it, I've seen better things go into my toilet.) But
still – they've all been touched by the hands of a true Genius. When you
become a member of the most exclusive club in the world, you will receive

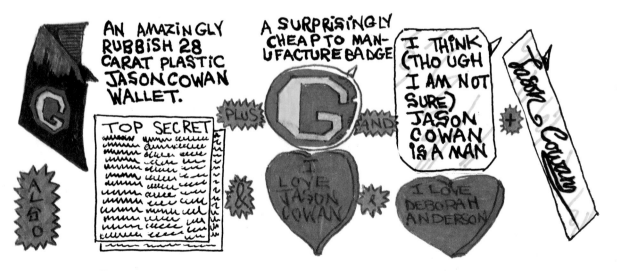

To join, all you have to do is send off our Questionnaire (completed of
course) together with a cheque/postal order for £99.99. Please allow a
long time for delivery.

QUESTIONNAIRE

Name

Address (and telephone number if you're an F and better looking than Deborah)

Sex   ☐ M   ☐ F   ☐ ?

Age

Religion ☐ Christian   ☐ Muslim   Jason Cowan   ☐ Other

I liked this book because _____

_____

or

I didn't like this book because _____

I thought it was ☐ expensive
                 ☐ very expensive

I think Jason Cowan should be _____
(eg worshipped)

I think Deborah Anderson should be _____

I hope Jason Cowan becomes
    ☐ Rich   ☐ Very Rich   ☐ A bit more modest

And I am ☐ glad
          ☐ not very glad
                    that I did my bit to help him.

I promise to worship and adore Jason Cowan for ever and ever and buy at lease ten copies of all his books.

Signed _____ (write your name here)

Parent's signature _____ (write your parent's name here)

Detach this form and send it with lots of money to
The Jason Cowan Fan Club
c/o Charles Herridge Ltd,
Woodacott, Northam, Bideford, Devon EX39 1NB.

YOU HAVE NOW REACHED THE END OF THIS BOOK.

What did you think of it, eh?
Is it: A milestone in childish depravity?
The hideous offspring of a sick mind?
The book that put the diced carrots into sick humour?
Yes, it's all this and more.

Think back. We've had constant degrading references to women and, indeed, highly embarrassing chauvinist pictures depicting women acting out my fantasies; constant references to drink, especially strong drink, ie whisky; crude references to parts of the body, eg grunties. And you loved it didn't you?

Well men, there's plenty more where that came from. My mind is a veritable cesspit of revolting ideas. All you have to do is buy hundreds of copies of this book — give them to your friends, wallpaper your bedroom with them, hang them on strings in the loo — and then write to my publisher demanding a sequel and I'll see what I can do. After all, I've got the Lamborghini on order and I've got to pay for it somehow!